Bill,
Christmas
12/21/75
Love
Amy & Stuart

Yorktown: Reflections on the Past

Melville I. Bryant, Jr.

Yorktown: Reflections on the Past

Melville I. Bryant, Jr.

PRELUDE

It is in the heat of the afternoon of a day in late summer, the year of our Lord 1753. The hot Virginia sun burns down from a cloudless sky and a sultry breeze from the river breathes against the shore. Small boats, merchantmen and men-of-war rise and fall in the harbor, a wave of motion, tugging at moorings, chafing against wharves. The shoreline is alive with movement. Sailors coiling ropes, climbing and pulling. Captains pacing the decks. Merchants and yeomen bargaining, arguing. Planters standing on the wharves, in an array of fashion, speculating prices, shipments and the ways of fortune. Englishmen giving commands. Slaves rolling hogsheads of tobacco into the holds of ships, sweating and grunting. Englishmen mopping their brows. The yeoman feeling the thin cloth on his back, the planter the great weight of responsibility, and the slave knowing only the hot sun and the coarsest rags about his loins. All feeling the heat. All dancing to the tune of tobacco. Men of substance letting thoughts fly to England where their fortunes hang in balance at the London market. Simple men tugging and straining, knowing only the moment. Some yearning to be free. Whether slave or no, all men serving the "sot weed," all men dependent on its whims. Tobacco is the lifeblood of the colony, the source of some men's slavery, the source of other men's freedom.

Young William Bland stands at the edge of the wharf, leaning and looking long over the water. Across the harbor, beyond the swaying forest of masts, the sunny green banks of Gloucester mark the far shore. In either direction the pale blue of the river York stretches as far as the eye can see. Upstream lie the great tobacco plantations and further still are the endless forests of the frontier. Downstream and beyond lies England, the ultimate end and hope of all colonial designs and expectations. Though he has never seen England's shores, the young man knows he is English.

His father, Thomas Peyton Bland, had journeyed to Virginia many years before, a Devonshire country lad eighteen years of age, led to these shores by seafarers' tales of the riches of the new lands. He had not found gold, but rather had discovered the rich Virginia soil and the strength within himself to prosper. Through years of travail and service to the Crown, Father is now a planter of great weight and substance in the colony. Father is many things: a planter, merchant and member of the House of

Burgesses, but above all he is an Englishman. A man does not easily forget the land of his birth. How often Father had sat in his chair, puffing a long clay pipe, remembering his boyhood, wondering where life would have led him had he never left Devon. Will can remember asking Father if he too was English. Father had laughed to himself amusedly, "Any son of an Englishman is English, my boy." Perhaps then it was true, Will was his father's countryman. The English law of primogeniture had already decided in his favor. As the eldest son Will was heir to a fortune in Virginia tobacco. His future decided by the fates of the English law, Will knew well the influence Britain had in Virginia. What future part England will play he cannot know. To a young man in Virginia, Britain seems silent, distant, an unknown giant riding the waves just beyond the horizon of the New World. How could the young man know that in years to come all men in Virginia would have to decide for themselves whether England or Virginia was their native land? The gateway to the New World, the great port of Yorktown, makes a huge noise around him, but the shadow of the leviathan, England falls across Virginia even in the heat of the day.

Back from the shore the wharves of Yorktown recede into a myriad of small buildings, tobacco houses, shops and streets lined with goods, warehouses, taverns, inns and ordinaries alive with the sights and sounds of the port in its most flourishing season. Horses, carts, carriages, dogs and servants move in all directions through the crowded streets. Men carrying trunks and barrels into shops. Merchants calling out their wares. Baking smells pouring from the open kitchen windows. The heavy taproom laughter of the English coming from the doorways. Young boys seated around an old sailor, listening to tales of stormy voyages and distant lands. A group of planters talking politics, arguing heatedly, the voice of Thomas Peyton Bland echoing powerfully in the deep tone that had singled him out, even in his early years, as a man born to lead.

"Gentlemen, we must always remember that Governor Dinwiddie is the representative of the Crown. Dinwiddie is not common rabble to be spat upon at our whim. We must remember that he carries the weight of the King behind him. If we wish to oppose his position in this matter we must respect the great office he commands."

"Pshaw, man!" says a thin-faced planter. "If a man treats me like rabble I'll treat him likewise — he may be the King's choice but a dog's a dog I say!"

"Calm yourself, man!" Bland answers. "Hotheads have no sway with me."

"But surely, Tom, you must agree that Dinwiddie's action is rash," a stout red-faced planter offers. "He cannot impose a tax on land patents without the approval of the burgesses. Where does he derive his authority?"

"The Crown, Thadeus, that is where he gets his authority . . ."

". . . and from rogues like you who let the bully have his way," the thin-faced man interrupts — shaking his finger at Bland.

"Watch your tongue, man, or I'll pluck it out for you!" Bland answers. "You miscreants should stay clear of politics."

The thin-faced planter mumbles something to his yeoman companion who chuckles to himself and grins curiously.

"But Thomas," continues the stout man, "we cannot stand idly by and let Dinwiddie take our gold while our hands are tied. One Spanish pistole may not be a large sum to a wealthy man, but it is the principle of it that I detest. Surely you cannot deny that all Englishmen have the right to tax themselves."

"No, Thadeus, I cannot deny our hereditary rights, nor do I wish to deny them — but you have hit upon a weighty point — neither can I deny that we are English. But some of you fellows, I'm afraid, are too quick to forget your King and country . . ."

". . . ay, he's a King's man alright," the yeoman interrupts. "The assembly is full of 'em. They'd let the Governor steal a continent from 'em without so much as a whimper."

"Zounds, fool! Such impudent fellows I've never beheld in all my days in the colony. What swaggering puppies you are! But you'll stand aside, I trow, when the great men stir."

"Pay them no mind," says Thadeus, "such brazen dogs bark in every alehouse in the colony — but tell me, Tom, how shall we succeed against the Governor?"

"Thadeus, if we are Englishmen, then we must use the God-given capacity for reason that is ours. The Governor will never be swayed by such hotheads as these surly fellows. If we wish to succeed then we must behave as reasonable men. The burgesses must petition the Governor with our requests and make persuasive arguments on the reasons for our dissent. Then, in all probability, the Governor will lift the tax. Prudent judgment is our advantage. In the end of this matter, as always, the reasonable heads will prevail."

"Egad!" cries the thin-faced man. "When great men stir I may very well move aside, but as for you, sir — I'll stand fast!"

"Zounds, sirrah! I've had enough of your insolence! Where's

my crop? I'll lash you knaves 'til you never dare insult a gentleman again!"

"Ecod!" shouts the yeoman. "Here comes another one of these King's men. Make haste, Jeremy!"

The sudden approach of a tall, stately gentleman scatters the agitators and quells the temper of Bland, who quickly puts away his riding crop.

"What's the matter here, Tom?" the tall man asks.

"I was just about to put an end to some wastrels when you arrived, Colonel. It seems these knaves and coxcombs are much abroad these days. A gentleman can't speak a breath about politics without some rascal shouting gibberish in his ear."

"Ay," the Colonel answers, "that is true. I never can catch the meaning of what these bullies say. They shout much, but make little sense."

"They're up in arms about the Governor's tax on land patents, Colonel Bolling," explains Thadeus. "They say we're bein' taxed without our consent and that the Governor is takin' away an Englishman's right to tax himself."

"But what does the Governor's Council think about it?" Bland asks, turning to the Colonel.

"Well, I advised the Governor against it," replies the Colonel, "for the good of the colony. But I concede that this taxation is entirely within his right. Dinwiddie is the King's man, you know."

"Within his right, Colonel?" replies Thadeus bluntly, "A cat and a fiddle! It's robbery I say!"

"Gentlemen! Gentlemen!" Bland implores them. "Let's have no more arguing today. I've had my fill."

"Ay," replies the Colonel, "and so have I. I'll hear no more on 't!"

"Well, what say you, gentlemen?" continues Bland. "Let's cool our tempers at the Swan. Will you gentlemen join me for a glass or two? Be my guests. What say you?"

The planters find this suggestion prodigiously agreeable and Thomas sends his man-servant down to the wharf to fetch Will to join their company.

In good spirits the small group of gentlemen make their way through the maze of streets, pausing for the passage of horses and the meeting of friends along the way. Beyond this labyrinth of roofs and chimneys built along a narrow strip of land next to the water's edge, the great marl bluffs of Yorktown rise high above the river and the port. Narrow streets lead up steep valleys to the peaceful village above the bank. Yorktown "above-the-hill" is the picture of gentility. Pleasant cottages and distinctive shops, known for the finest English goods, line Main Street under the shade of giant willows and tulip poplars. Behind ivied garden walls the great Georgian mansions rise above the trees, their tall windows casting proud reflections toward the river. Through a secluded gate one may find ladies and gentlemen bowling on the green or Secretary Nelson enjoying his pipe in the cool privacy of his boxwood garden. Yorktown is a seat of refinement and power in the New World. The stately brick courthouse, its lofty cupola surveying the whole of the village, is a symbol of the order and reason that is here. Across Main Street is the Swan Tavern, one of the most famous public houses in the colony, the center for news in the town, and a meeting place for all men in the prosperous stations of life. Some say that the distance between the wharf below and the proud Swan above is not the length of so many crunching steps up the hill on Ballard Street, but rather is measured by the difference between the poor yeoman and the wealthy planter. By either standard it is a great distance, but in this New World not an impossible journey for a man with strong legs and a stout heart....

... now the chilled Madeira of the Swan but a memory to the lips, the goodly company parted, the entourage of Thomas Peyton Bland, planter, heads down a narrow, wheel-rutted road toward home. Bland and his son, followed by the overseer, are on horseback, the servants behind in the heavy wagon. It is now late afternoon and, passing through the great fields surrounding Yorktown, Will feels the leather hard against his legs, the sinking sun in his squinting eyes, and the strength of the animal's tightening haunches beneath him. The dust stirring, Will loosens his high collar, breathing a long-awaited sigh. Teams of oxen pass by and now and then the humble dwelling of a poor farmer. Soon they have left the green fields far behind under the dark shade of the forest, passing by ancient oaks, their trunks as large in girth as a yeoman's cottage. The deep wood answers the clopping of the hooves, echoing and re-echoing on either side, game darting for brush just ahead. Occasionally passing the cedar lane of a great plantation, its gate crowned with the pineapple finial so common in Virginia and said to be a sign of hospitality. The travel is slow. Now and then the forest road sinks into deep ravines and low marshes, losing its way in the oozing ruts of wheels gone by.

Thomas Bland, his head held high, riding proud to the front, the fine animal and he as one. His hooded eyes watching the woods to left and right, capturing a fleeting glimpse of the afternoon sunlight piercing the dark corners of the forest. The tobacco time mainly behind him now, the summer nearly spent, and his hopes riding the waves with the captain of a British merchantman. Fortune has been kind, tarried long with him, but it has not always been so. Bland knows, as well as any man, of time's mutability and he longs for this world to look well on his son. But that is a matter for another lifetime and the strength left him now will serve to the end but no more. He has lived in an age of good fortune. The colony is stronger now. Wherever he casts his glance there are plantations and Englishmen, living a good life, order and reason prevailing. In this afternoon of late summer the man is tired, but satisfied with the accomplishments of life. With his wife and daughters at home, Will strong, the King on the throne of England and God in His heaven, he will easily close his eyes when that final moment comes at last, expectantly listening for the music of the spheres . . . .

Will, riding effortlessly in the wake of his father, his blue eyes a haze of wondering. The future being his, the past seems to have belonged to someone else. A small boy perhaps, grown strong riding and hunting in the Virginia wood, grown a man, but without the grim lines of care so deeply etched in the brow of the tough-skinned overseer. He has known nature long, has observed its creatures, its ceaseless movements, the changing of its seasons, and has known freedom in the New World. Will has no memories of England past, his father carrying them forever to the grave at his death, and while he is still young enough to love, the Age of Reason at its summit, men seem in perfect harmony with God's creatures, all knowing the same master. Now Father's words seem true. With the promise of an hospitable Virginia before him, planters and ladies in fine apparel, great Georgian plantation houses along the river, the tobacco weed growing well in the field, and the strong back of the black man to till the rich earth, order prevails and there is hope for tomorrow.

The last rustling and singing of the birds overhead is almost done and a deepening sky shrouds the last pale twilight. The sun, moments before a simmering red coal through the far wood, has now gone under. The forest is silent but for the soft music of the black men and the rolling of the wagon. Down a long lane a light shines from the window of a great house. The day ends and the tall gate at Waterview is reached at dusk.

. . . years later . . . it is 1781 . . . a stirring of men in the early hours of morning. A faint light flickering through the drop of a tent. Inside, the light still dim and a large man resting on a worn cot. Will Bland, his face lined now with the cares of a man of forty-five, a strong body weakened with years of war. His eyes a flash of light in the darkness. There is no time for sleep now, nor was there any last night. The cannons had pounded through the night, bursting and thundering, flashing red against the black sky. In the deep of the night, thoughts of Father had come back to him. The old, proud man riding the great chestnut down the dusty road to Waterview. How far away he seems now, another world altogether then. All seemed well. What would Father say if he could see him now — his once-young body spent with the passing of years, his hair grown grey, Waterview but a hollow shell now — the soil weak from too much 'bacca, and his fortune spent on the cause? Well thank God Father's in his grave. Wouldn't care to have him see me before Yorktown, blasting and battering the town with artillery fire. And thank God for Washington, too, would have wasted a life and fortune — and nothing to show for it — without that man. In the early light of the day, Will collects himself from the cot and reaches for his uniform in the dark of the tent. A voice calls at the door, "Colonel Bland sir!"

"Coming, Major! . . . ."

. . . it is ten o'clock on the morning of October the seventeenth. The eighteen and twenty-four-pound cannons, the mortars, the howitzers, are incessantly pounding away at the British positions in Yorktown, as they have for eight long days. Suddenly there is a quiet. A hush runs through the siege lines. The Colonel raises his head, his eyes search the distance. A drummer in red steps to the parapet on the British line and beats a parley. A white flag is waved. The siege has ended . . . .

. . . looking back on it all, an old Will Bland sits on the south porch at Waterview under the shade of a tall grove of tulip poplars planted in a distant age. The year is 1800 and a lifetime has passed since Father and the young Will had ridden horseback to Yorktown . . . standing on the tobacco wharf . . . hearing the voices of the planters . . . watching the world as it was, not unlike the world Raleigh or John Smith had known . . . yes, we were all Englishmen then.

Remembering Father's words before the war, "Reason, my boy, always use reason . . . it separates men from the animals . . . it is your humanity." How as a young man he had thought Father held the secrets to the workings of the universe within his grey head. But Father's world seems so distant now. The years of the colony seem strange and foreign, a fleeting dream in the days of one's youth. But what had wrought the change?— where had he and Father parted? As an old man looking back, Will could not know for certain — but one moment, a fleeting heartbeat in youth, had stood out clearly, briefly from the myriad of passing years and faces. Remembering . . . it was a clear, cold night in late autumn . . . Father had called him into the study . . . handed him a small, worn copy of Alexander Pope . . . Father saying, "I think you are at the age now when you can gain from this — it has been food for much thought to me these past few years — I hope you shall learn something from it tonight . . . ."

. . . Will had gone into the drawing room . . . remembering the words . . .

Vast Chain of Being! which from God began,
Natures ethereal, human, angel, man,
Beast, bird, fish, insect, what no eye can see,
No glass can reach! from Infinite to thee,
From thee to nothing . . . .

. . . realizing what Father had been echoing all these years . . .
the source of his convictions, the workings of his world had
become suddenly clear . . . but then he knew that something
was awry . . . something missing . . . had Father read his own
words into Pope's essay? Had he seen Pope's universe of natural
order only through the eyes of his wealth and class? The prevailing order . . . was it the natural order? Will could only
speculate . . . .
. . . and then he had been stirred by something in his blood,
drawing him close to nature . . . he had gone to the window,
raised the sash . . . the darkness was cold and penetrating . . .
hearing the cries of the wild geese . . . thousands of them passing before the face of the full moon . . . passing through the
clear, cold air above the river . . . for a moment his spirit had
seemed to fly free with them . . . the great wings rising and fall-
ing . . . the wind . . . rushing . . . . All of his being seemed suddenly lost, all of the past was swept away, the future seemed distant, clouded. The moment became all . . . until he was aware
only of the wind and the thread that links all of nature . . . that
makes him kinsman to the geese . . . . And then they had passed,
and with them the words and wisdom of the world seemed to
pass away . . . Father's world was fading . . . .
And then those years of growing into manhood, watching
Father grow more furious with every new breach with England,
his incessant appeals for reason, while men were using the very
reason Father worshipped to tear apart the order of his universe. Britain had stood upon its absolute right to sovereignty
over the colonies, using what it called order and reason to sanc-
tion tyranny. But it could not have been the reason taught by
nature, for nature will have her way in the end and, as the Englishmen discovered, it is always a rough course to steer against
her sovereignty. The colonists had merely pursued reason in its
natural and logical course, to its ultimate and earth-shaking
conclusion. The acts of Britain were opposed, castigated and
condemned. At the height of the debate there was Father . . .
making his last appeal to his son . . . Will watching the old man

torn with rage, pulling a dusty volume down from the high shelf
. . . saying, "If you will not heed me, I beseech you to consider
this — turn against me if you will — but heed the portent of
Shakespeare," for a moment his eyes piercing into the eyes of
his son, then whispering his last warning, "Take but degree
away, untune that string, and hark, what discord follows! Each
thing meets in mere oppugnancy." But then Father had died in
January 1775, months before the firing of the first shots at Lex-
ington and Concord. He did not live to see the storm, and with
his passing — the age itself passed on.

Recalling the soul-searching of the people — some men re-
turning to the land of their birth, others turning into Americans,
leaving Britain in their wake. Soon it was too late for turning
back. Travelling to Philadelphia with Thomas Nelson in the
summer of 1776, remembering the words of Thomas Paine —
signalling the inevitability of war:

> But Britain is the parent country, say some. Then the more
> shame upon her conduct. Even brutes do not devour their
> young, nor savages make war upon their families . . . . Re-
> conciliation is *now* a fallacious dream. Nature has deserted
> the connection . . . .

How those words had rung through his mind in the years that
followed . . . "Nature has deserted the connection . . ." or, as
he had often thought later, Father and his Englishmen had deserted their connection with nature. But then it was not hard to
understand Father's loyalties. Father had spent his childhood
in England, he had never seen the Virginia wood through the
eyes of a young boy. When he had journeyed across the Atlantic
to first view the great forests of the wilderness, he had carried
the memories of England within his mind. To Father, the wilderness was important because it could be conquered and develop-
ed for the glory of the Mother Country. To Will, who had grown
up in the Virginia wood and had seen the wonders of nature at
an early age, the wilderness was a great teacher he would heed
and follow his entire life. Perhaps that accounted for the different course his life had taken. Father had pledged his loyalty
to England, while Will's allegiance was to nature. It is not then
surprising that his voice would join the cries of his countrymen
when they sought to form a natural alliance.

The Continental Army had become his life after Father died
and nothing was left to restrain him from following his con-

science. Days of encampment, moving in the night, striking, ever keeping away from the main front of the British forces. Frozen winters, uniforms wearing thin . . . letters from his wife telling of Waterview's steady decline, fields unplowed, debts unpaid. Wondering what kind of legacy he would leave to his own son.

But then came Yorktown. He was already an old man when it finally happened, but perhaps made more deserving by the waiting. Remembering the British grounding arms at the great surrender on that day when the world turned upside down. Seeing great Washington towering above even the haughty British. At the sight of surrender after years of fighting, waiting, hoping, he knew freedom had been worth its price.

When Will's eyes close at life's last breath and his body is lowered deep into the Virginia soil beside Father in the shadowy graveyard at Waterview, he will not await the music of the spheres . . . perhaps only images of this world darkening . . . voices fading . . . Waterview . . . Englishmen . . . cannons pounding . . . then quiet . . . a hush along the lines . . . only the sound of the wind . . . rushing . . . .

REFLECTIONS

Today, Yorktown is a mere shadow of the busy port village that flourished in the eighteenth century. Only a few weathered buildings remain to testify to the prosperous age Yorktown knew at the height of the colonial period. The Englishmen who once thrived here have gone long ago, but they have left the cultural shell of their colonial civilization, the gardens, the art, the architecture, behind. History, in passing, has indeed left its indelible mark upon Yorktown. The Siege of 1781 had such a devastating effect on Yorktown that it soon thereafter lost its prominence as a cultural and commercial center and began its gradual decline into forgotten obscurity. Just as the Battle of Yorktown gave life to the new American Nation, it just as surely put an end to the civilization that had flourished here. Like many other towns which had figured prominently in the life of the colony, Yorktown naturally lost its reason to be as Americans looked westward to the building of a new nation.

Today, aside from being the seat of county government for York County, Yorktown's chief commodity is its heritage. The community that exists here today is much smaller than the port town which thrived in the eighteenth century. Yorktown past and Yorktown present are two different towns and they inhabit two different worlds. But one thing remains virtually unchanged. The natural setting of the town today remains much like the town that Thomas Nelson knew. Great trees still line its streets. Garden gates still turn to reveal a world of flowers in the spring. The English boxwood that Virginia is so known for still grows in abundance here. The changings of the four seasons are still strongly felt, each season having a distinctly pleasing quality of its own. Most of all, the York River still flows past its marl banks in moody seclusion. In a chaotic twentieth century world, Yorktown is indeed an unusual place.

Perhaps the most extraordinary thing about Yorktown is that it seems always to exist in a twilight world halfway between fantasy and reality. The eighteenth and the twentieth centuries seem as though they are always trying to merge. There is an eighteenth-century world at Yorktown that is trying to make its presence known. There are times in Yorktown when one cannot be certain which century he is living in. The distant past and the present often seem as one. The visitor is often startled when he first begins to notice this time distortion. But it is there. The few original buildings that remain speak of a simpler and more gracious age when beauty and practicality were one. The voice of eighteenth-century Yorktown beckons to the inhabitants of the twentieth century. It is perhaps those of us who believe in the value of the past who must listen. Observe the old homes of Yorktown. Walk down its shaded lanes. Enter its gardens. Feel the light Virginia wind coming from the river, brushing the tops of the great trees. Listen for the sound of a distant, fleeting hoofbeat, a faint clop of boot leather on an ancient walk and turn to find . . . nothing. Let the ghosts whisper in your ear in the still quiet of Yorktown . . . the past is speaking to you . . . .

Today, the village is merely a faded reflection of colonial Yorktown . . .

. . . through which we may journey to the eighteenth century.

The atmosphere of the distant past . . .

. . . lingers in the quiet streets.

The height of Yorktown's prosperity as a port city came in the middle of the eighteenth century which saw its development as a flourishing center for the merchant's trade. Many small stores did a thriving business along Main Street, including the Medical Shop, above, which was reconstructed by the National Park Service in 1936.

Few of Yorktown's original buildings have survived the passage of two centuries, but those that remain bear witness to the affluence of its colonial citizens. Richard Ambler's brick storehouse, above, has come to be called the "Customhouse" because Ambler was collector of customs for the port of Yorktown during the second quarter of the eighteenth century. The Dudley Digges House, below, dates from about 1750 and is one of the few wooden buildings that survived the bombardment of 1781. The York County Courthouse, opposite, is a recent addition to Yorktown, having been completed in 1955. It is the fifth courthouse to stand on the same site and resembles the design of the Courthouse of 1733, which was destroyed by fire in 1814.

The delicate proportions of the Georgian houses . . .

. . . are further softened by the lush green of the Virginia landscape.

Each window seems to watch the garden world outside and to reflect the changings of the seasons in its glass.

Yorktown is indeed a world of gardens, both great and small, formal and natural. Through a beckoning gate one may find an abundance of seasonal color, such as the spectacular Edmund Smith House garden, above, at the height of tulip time.

Cherries ripen in the sunlight near Nelson Street. ➡

Wisteria and wild flowers haunt the wilderness graveyard at nearby Ringfield Plantation.

A rose clings to the ivied wall of the Edmund Smith House garden.

A secluded window witnesses the arrival of the day lilies.

A field of marigolds at the Nelson House.

iris

dahlia

magnolia

English daisies

peony

camellia

SWAN TAVERN

The Swan was the best known of the many taverns in colonial Yorktown. Travellers found the Swan a comfortable place for lodging and there they could be served rum, ale, Madeira wine, a heavy fare of small game from the nearby woodlands and a variety of seafood from local waters. Destroyed by an ammunition explosion during the Civil War, the present Swan was reconstructed by the National Park Service in 1935.

The glow from the hearth shines in the pewter.

A warm fireside in the Swan tap-room was a welcomed sight to colonial travellers during the winter months.

In a more sober mood a traveller could well have written home from a secretary such as this in the Swan drawing room.

Furnishings courtesy of Swan Tavern Antiques

In the long, lazy days of summer the village is an oasis of green beside the pale blue of the York River. The humidity that the Tidewater is so known for is especially felt here because of Yorktown's proximity to the water. The moisture in the air increases the effect of the heat, and life accordingly slows to a crawl under the hot summer sun.

The Thomas Pate House, below, is one of Yorktown's oldest homes, dating from the very beginning of the eighteenth century.

The Nelson House still bears the scars of the Siege, when it was heavily damaged during the bombardment. A cannonball remains embedded in the east wall.

NELSON HOUSE

This large Georgian residence was built before 1745 by "Scotch Tom" Nelson. It was inherited later in the century by his famous grandson, General Thomas Nelson, Jr., patriot, governor of Virginia, signer of the Declaration of Independence, and commander of the militia at the Battle of 1781.

Everywhere you turn in June, on the banks of the river . . .

... and along the picket fence at the Dudley Digges House, the purple "York-town Onion" rears its shaggy head.

GRACE CHURCH

Since its construction in 1697, Grace Church has continued to be a place of worship and today serves the York-Hampton Parish of the Episcopal Diocese of Southern Virginia. In its shaded churchyard lie many of the sons and daughters of colonial Yorktown, including General Thomas Nelson, Jr.

MOORE HOUSE

In the parlor of the private home of Augustine Moore, above, commissioners from the allied and British forces met on October 18, 1781, to draft the Articles of Capitulation, which stated the terms of the British surrender.

Constructed about 1725, the Moore farmhouse lay just behind the first allied siege line, one mile east of Yorktown along the river shore. It is typical of the many small plantations which surrounded the village at the time of the Siege of 1781. The icehouse, above, was a familiar plantation structure throughout the colony. The commodious dining room, left, attests to Moore's prosperity. Though not a man of great wealth, Moore was a successful merchant and planter in the business firm of the Nelson family.

Gradually, the last heat of the Indian summer . . .

. . . fades in the first changing of the leaves of a gnarled paper mulberry tree . . . and then . . .

. . . suddenly the town bursts into the many-colored tapestry of autumn.

The first breath of cool autumn air chills the early morning in the village . . .

. . . and the newly bared branches reveal the surrounding woodlands turning to golden brown.

The fields take on a fresh beauty in this time of harvest, a sign of the seasons and of a yielding to nature's dominion.

Slowly, the color of autumn fades . . .

. . . and days grow colder into the first touch of winter.

SESSIONS HOUSE
The arrival of winter is warmed by a blazing fire in the drawing room hearth of the oldest home in Yorktown. Thomas Sessions built this house during the last decade of the seventeeth century and it is one of the very few remaining structures dating from before 1700.

The Christmas season is welcomed by traditional trimmings at the Swan Tavern, opposite, and at the Somerwell House, above.

Lanterns were important features of Yorktown homes in colonial days. Today, their electrified counterparts still offer a guiding light to night-time travellers.

Snow rarely falls in Yorktown, but when it does, it further reduces the distance between the present and the colonial past. Snow-bound, Yorktown seems to dwell in a timeless winter world of its own that knows nothing of the busy twentieth-century world beyond. As today's inhabitants dig out from under the storm, they too feel the bite of winter's fury and know, if only for a moment, what it means to be slave to the elements and not master over them. Along Main Street and at the Nelson House, above, the eighteenth century is now as close as a footprint in the newly fallen snow . . . .

Along Nelson Street ➡

A snow-covered gateway opens on Main Street and you may enter knowing that the turn of a gate in Yorktown will always reveal the past that lingers here . . . .

EPILOGUE

Yorktown will always hold a special place in the history of America. The community that flourished in Yorktown during the eighteenth century represented the height of the British colonial civilization in America. Yorktown during the Age of Reason must have indeed been a paradise of genteel refinement. But, it seems, life must not have been perfect enough for its citizens. Despite their prosperity under the rule of Britain, Yorktown's citizens became some of the most vehement rebels against the Crown. General Thomas Nelson, Jr., exemplified this quality when he turned the allied guns against his own home in Yorktown during the Siege. Nelson, like other citizens of Yorktown, gave his entire fortune to the Revolutionary cause. Perhaps we will never know just how much the patriots valued that nineteenth day of October 1781, when the defeated British army under the command of Lord Cornwallis marched down York-Hampton Road between the columns of victorious French and American troops. We can never know what each American soldier felt as he watched the army of the mightiest military nation in the world ground arms and surrender to his ragged Continental Army. Looking back from the 1970's, with the perspective that the passage of two centuries has given us, it is readily apparent that the American Nation actually began right there on the battlefields surrounding Yorktown. The victory at Yorktown represented the ultimate defeat of monarchical will in America and breathed life into the written word of the Declaration of Independence. Yorktown converted a handful of rebellious colonists into the forefathers of the greatest nation in history and their triumphant dream — the sovereignty of the people — has become the hope of the world.